Mad and Miraculous Inventions

Interactive Quiz

Managing Editors: Simon Melhuish and Sarah Wells

Series Editor: Nikole G Bamford

Designer: Linley J Clode

Writer: Gwen McCann

Cover design: Radio

Published by
The Lagoon Group
PO Box 311, KT2 5QW, UK
PO Box 990676, Boston, MA 02199, USA

ISBN: 190479758X

www.intelliquestbooks.com

Printed in China

IntelliQuest

UNIQUE BOOK CODE	001

Instructions

First of all make sure you
have a Quizmo –

Find the book's unique code (this
appears at the top of this page).
Use the < and > buttons to scroll
to this number on the Quizmo screen.
Press the ⬅ button to enter the
code, and you're ready to go.

Use the < > scroll buttons to select
the question number you want to
answer. Press the A, B, C, or D
button to enter your chosen answer.

If you are correct the green light beside
the button you pressed will flash. You can then
use the scroll button to move on to another question.

If your answer is incorrect, the red light beside the
button you pressed will flash.

Don't worry, you can try again and again until you have the correct answer, OR move on to another question. (Beware: the more times you guess incorrectly, the lower your final percentage score will be!)

You can finish the quiz at any point – just press the 🔙 button to find out your score and rank as follows:

75% or above	Caution – genius at work!
50% – 74%	You are a mental giant – keep at it!
25% – 49%	You're not too sharp – try harder!
Less than 25%	This is the 21st century – are you with us?

If you do press the 🔙 button to find out your score, this will end your session and you will have to use the 🔙 to start again!

HAVE FUN!

001

Name the inventor and the invention whose first prototype included a coffin lid, a biscuit tin, knitting needles, string and sealing wax as components?

- **A)** John Logie Baird - television
- **B)** Thomas Edison - phonograph
- **C)** Marconi - radio
- **D)** Alva Fisher - washing machine

002

Which patent is reckoned to be the most valuable ever?

- **A)** Alexander Graham Bell's first telephone patent
- **B)** Guglielmo Marconi's first radio patent
- **C)** John Logie Baird's first television patent
- **D)** Lionel Hoover's first vacuum cleaner

003

Who invented and built the first powered boat that could reach Australia from the UK without refueling?

- **A)** George Stephenson
- **B)** Karl Benz
- **C)** Wilbur Wright
- **D)** Isambard Kingdom Brunel

Which inventor, fascinated by electricity, flew a kite attached to a wire in a thunderstorm to prove that lightning was a form of electricity?

A) Benjamin Franklin
B) Thomas Edison
C) Allesandro Volta
D) Michael Faraday

US President Garfield was shot in the leg by an assassin - an eminent inventor used his new invention, the metal detector, to try and locate the bullet - unfortunately all he found were the metal bedsprings. Who was that inventor?

A) Benjamin Franklin
B) Robert Stephenson
C) Alexander Graham Bell
D) Thomas Edison

Who said 'Genius is one percent inspiration and 99 percent perspiration?'

A) Thomas Edison
B) George Stephenson
C) Benjamin Franklin
D) Leonardo da Vinci

004

005

006

007

Like many amazing inventions the inspiration for the microwave was an accident. A scientist working on a radar research project noticed something strange when walking past a magnetron what was it?

A) His cup of coffee boiled over
B) A chocolate bar in his pocket melted
C) A metal pin in his leg tingled
D) The ice in his drink melted

008

What invention was called a 'device of Satan' and psychiatrists predicted that it would drive you mad?

A) The phonograph
B) The television
C) The radio
D) The telephone

009

Inventing something is usually a laborious process. James Dyson set out to invent a bagless vacuum cleaner; it took him 14 years. How many prototypes did he build?

A) 10,000
B) 5,000
C) 500
D) 100

General Electrical

Alexander Graham Bell died in 1922; what was done in America to honor his passing?

- **A)** All phones rang for one minute
- **B)** Electricity was switched off for one minute
- **C)** All phones were silent for one minute
- **D)** All radios were silent for one minute

010

What did John Logie Baird invent to help alleviate his suffering - what was it?

- **A)** Gloves with integral warming pads
- **B)** Padded trousers for the relief of piles
- **C)** Knee brace to support weak kneecaps
- **D)** Medicated socks

011

John Logie Baird decided that he could invent a process for making diamonds - what was the unfortunate side effect of this?

- **A)** He blew off his left little finger
- **B)** He destroyed a very valuable diamond ring
- **C)** He electrocuted himself and ended up in hospital
- **D)** He blacked out half of Glasgow

012

013

What is considered the most important invention in the history of mankind?

    A) Fire
    B) The wheel
    C) The printing press
    D) The loin cloth

014

Archimedes is the most famous ancient inventor, although mathematics was probably his first love. He invented some deadly weapons to stop the attacking Roman army. Which of these was not one of Archimedes' inventions?

    A) Giant mirrors to reflect the sun's rays to set fire to things
    B) Giant catapult that could fire 500lb boulders
    C) Giant claws that could lift boats out of the water
    D) Giant cannon that fired huge lead cannon balls

015

Which of these came first?
    A) Silk
    B) Glass
    C) Candle
    D) Soap

Ancient Inventions

The first evidence of writing in the West appeared in Sumeria, Iraq in about 3,000 B.C. - what was the purpose of this writing?

    A) A shopping list
    B) Counting sheep
    C) The record of a battle
    D) A poem about rain

There have been people on Earth since about 2.6 million years B.C. - when did the wheel first appear?

    A) 1,000,000 B.C.
    B) 3,500 B.C.
    C) 35,000 B.C.
    D) 1,500 B.C.

What was the first completely manufactured musical instrument - it appeared in Ur in Sumeria in 4500 B.C.?

    A) Stringed harp
    B) Hunting horn
    C) Bagpipe
    D) Oliphant

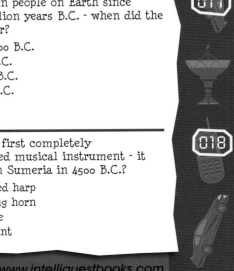

019

Christopher Sholes invented the typewriter keyboard as we know it today – what is his keyboard known as?

A) Alphabetical
B) Qwerty
C) Sholes
D) Phonetic

020

A pair of brothers invented the ballpoint pen in 1894, what was their surname?

A) Bic
B) Stylo
C) Parker
D) Biro

021

Which of these was invented first?

A) Paperclip
B) Stapler
C) Rubber bands
D) Safety pin

Johan Vaaler, a Norwegian inventor filed the first patent for a paperclip in 1899, the paperclip went on to have another significance in Norway, what was it?

A) It was worn as a symbol of a radical underground socialist party

B) It was worn as a symbol of protest against the occupying German army

C) It was sent in letters as a sign of love

D) Gold ones were given as an engagement present

Christopher Sholes took out several patents for typewriters - his first typewriter was less than ideal, which of these was one of its drawbacks?

A) It was the size of a small piano

B) You had to hit the keys with a small hammer

C) The keys hit the paper underneath so you couldn't read the typing

D) You only got a negative image of the typing which then had to be printed

024

Today about 14 million Bic ballpoint pens are sold every day but when ballpoint pens were first sold in the US they were a novelty - how much did they cost in today's money?

A) $70
B) $270
C) $570
D) $2,700

025

For what job was the first adhesive cellophone tape invented?

A) House painting
B) Spray painting cars
C) Mending china
D) Mending books

026

George de Mestral came up with a great invention after a nature hike in the country with his dog - what was it?

A) The zip
B) The pogo stick
C) Velcro
D) Sellotape

Who seem to have invented false teeth (carved from bone or ivory or recycled human teeth)?

A) The Greeks 200 B.C.
B) The Etruscans 700 B.C.
C) The Victorians 1840 A.D.
D) The Romans 100 A.D.

The first mention of a toothbrush is in a Chinese Encyclopedia in 1498 - these brushes had bone or bamboo handles, what hair were the bristles made from?

A) Squirrels
B) Porcupines
C) Hogs
D) Pandas

Toothbrushes have been invented and re-invented since they became popular in Europe. How many different kinds of toothbrushes have been patented?

A) 100
B) 400
C) 1,000
D) 2,000

Teeth

030

The Romans invented toothpaste and mouthwash - there was one ingredient that was particularly highly prized for its bleaching qualities - what was it?

A) Spanish anchovy essence
B) Spanish fermented vinegar
C) Portuguese urine
D) French cheese mold

031

Many inventive minds have wrestled with false teeth - in the 18th century ivory was popular but it rotted and tasted horrible. All kinds of things were tried, which of these animal's teeth were popular for a while?

A) Hippopotamus
B) Elephant
C) Cow
D) Pig

032

In 1770 Alexis Duchateau made a breakthrough with false teeth - what was it?

A) Metal teeth
B) Rubber gums
C) Porcelain teeth
D) Transplanting dead-men's teeth

Fashion

033

The film director D.W. Griffith was anxious to make his leading lady look more appealing. What did he invent in 1916 to achieve his aim?

- **A)** Stiletto heels
- **B)** False eyelashes
- **C)** False breasts
- **D)** Curlers

034

What invention caused a fashion craze in the middle of the 19th century?

- **A)** Mauve dye
- **B)** The stiletto heel
- **C)** The zip
- **D)** Red lipstick

035

Thirteenth century Germany saw the invention of something that changed what we wore forever - what was it?

- **A)** Silk weaving
- **B)** The zip
- **C)** The buttonhole
- **D)** The spinning wheel

036

Charles Macintosh was experimenting with the waste products of a gasworks when he invented a waterproof material. The Mackintosh, as it became known, had various drawbacks - which of these wasn't one?

    A) It smelt
    B) It shrank in the rain
    C) It was stiff in cold weather
    D) It was sticky in hot weather

037

What was special about the lipstick invented in 1920 by Preston Sturges, a Hollywood film director?

    A) It glowed in the dark
    B) It was waterproof
    C) It was permanent
    D) It was kiss-proof

038

What year did the stiletto heel appear?

    A) 1953
    B) 1853
    C) 1753
    D) 1653

039

Up until the beginning of the 20th century women had to wear restrictive, uncomfortable underwear - in 1913 an American socialite rebelled and got her maid to create her a brassiere - what did the maid use?

A) Two silk purses and some ribbon

B) Two handkerchiefs and some ribbon

C) Two silk stockings and some ribbon

D) Two cups and sellotape

040

What inspired the Rev William Lee to invent the stocking frame, the first practical knitting machine?

A) He hated the feel of his wife's coarse stockings

B) His fiancée was more interested in knitting than in him

C) His fiancée was a bad knitter and her stockings were always full of holes

D) His wife suffered from bad arthritis and found it painful to knit

041 Morse code began the revolution in long distance communication - what was the first Morse code message?

A) What God hath wrought
B) May God be praised!
C) Do you read me?
D) Good evening Mr Brown

042 Guglielmo Marconi spent a long time tinkering away with his radio wave machine - what did he first get radio waves to do?

A) Sound a horn
B) Ring a bell
C) Crackle and hiss
D) Say 'Hello'

043 Marconi lived on a big estate in Italy - he sent radio messages to his brother who was about a mile away. How did his brother signal that he had received the message?

A) By sounding a horn
B) By firing a gun
C) By letting off a firework
D) By shining a torch

Communications

What did Marconi use as an aerial for his first transatlantic broadcast?

A) A huge dish
B) A tall metal pole
C) A huge kite
D) A telephone

Who was the first person to appear on television?

A) John Logie Baird
B) Mrs Margaret McCann (housekeeper)
C) Winston Churchill
D) William Taynton (office boy)

What year did the first video recorder appear?

A) 1950
B) 1960
C) 1956
D) 1966

047 The first electric light bulbs invented were very unreliable, but they also had another problem that made them unsuitable for domestic use, what was it?

    A) They flickered on and off all the time

    B) They were too dim and only gave off as much light as a single candle

    C) They were too bright so could only be used for lighthouses and in the streets

    D) They were really expensive

---

048 Count Alessandro Volta invented the battery in 1800. What was the problem with his invention?

    A) There was nothing invented that the power could be used for

    B) The power it created was too unreliable

    C) The power it created was too strong

    D) It used such expensive materials that no one could afford to make one

Thomas Edison tested hundreds of possible filaments for light bulbs - one of his most successful was a specially-treated cotton that glowed for 13.5 hours. How long should a modern light bulb last?

A) 100 hours
B) 500 hours
C) 750 hours
D) 1,000 hours

Benjamin Franklin coined many of the terms we associate with electricity, including negative, positive and conductor; which of these terms is also one of his?

A) The Volt
B) The Watt
C) The plug
D) The battery

Which of these was invented in 1843, although it took many more technological changes for it to catch on?

A) Telephone answering machine
B) The fax machine
C) The mobile phone
D) The x-ray

052

How long was it from the first demonstration of electric light to the first electric bulbs going on sale?

    A) 110 years
    B) 80 years
    C) 40 years
    D) 16 years

053

Magnetrons were used by radar operators to detect aircraft up to 200 miles away. They are now the power source used in microwave ovens. What other use did radar operators put their magnetrons to in the World War II?

    A) Frying eggs
    B) Warming their feet
    C) Heating water for tea
    D) Warming their beds

054

The first electricity company was started in New York in 1882 - how many customers did it have?

    A) 2
    B) 52
    C) 82
    D) 112

Telephone

Johann Phillip Reis invented an early "telephon," it was made up of a strange collection of parts - which of these was not part of the original design?

055

    A) A cork

    B) A knitting needle

    C) A sausage skin

    D) An ear trumpet

What did Alexander Graham Bell (the inventor of the telephone) do before he started inventing?

056

    A) An engineer

    B) An actor

    C) A teacher of the deaf

    D) A bell ringer

Alexander Graham Bell managed to build a telephone receiver (the bit you hear with) before a transmitter (the bit you speak into); what was an essential part of his first successful transmitter?

057

    A) A sausage skin

    B) A spinning disc

    C) A container of acid

    D) A bowl of water

058

The first telephone message was an accident, Alexander Graham Bell spoke on the phone before he realized that his invention worked; what did he say?

    A) Fire!
    B) Tell my wife I would like chops
    C) Where did you put my glasses?
    D) Mr Watson, come here, I want you

059

Alexander Graham Bell won the race to patent an effective telephone. A rival inventor, Elisha Gray was just hours behind him with his patent. Gray never gave up pursuing Bell and his invention - what did he do to him?

    A) Served him with 600 lawsuits
    B) Tried to destroy his workshop
    C) Rang him 100 times a day
    D) Kidnapped Bell's children

060

What year was the cell phone invented?
    A) 1947
    B) 1957
    C) 1967
    D) 1977

A pparently Alexander the Great used submersible vessels as far back as 332 B.C. James I watched a demonstration of the first known submarine; it was propeled by oars but what was the vessel coated in?

A) Rubber
B) Copper
C) Leather
D) Iron

061

T he first steamboat took its maiden voyage in 1783; it was considered a great success although it only lasted 15 minutes - what happened to it?

A) It took in lots of water and sank
B) It ran into a pier
C) It shook itself apart
D) The engine exploded

062

E dmond Halley is known for his interest in comets mostly but which of these was his aquatic invention?

A) Diving bell
B) Aqualung
C) Submarine
D) Paddle steamer

063

064

Submarines were used to great effect in the American War of Independence but one invention in the 1950s transformed their usefulness - making them an essential part of any modern navy. What was it?

A) Jet engines
B) Compressed air
C) Lightweight plastic
D) Nuclear power

065

Sir Isambard Kingdom Brunel built a steamship called the 'Great Western' - it was the first steam ship to cross the Atlantic - how long did it take to complete its first voyage?

A) 15 hours
B) 5 days
C) 15 days
D) 1.5 weeks

066

What were the first life jackets made of?

A) Balloons
B) Balsa wood
C) Pig skins full of air
D) Cork

067

The basic bicycle mechanism has inspired inventors to come up with many spin-off inventions. One that the inventor was convinced was going to be popular in schools and sports clubs was called the Vélo-douche - what was it?

A) A swimming pool cleaning system powered by bicycle

B) A mop and floor polishing system powered by bicycle

C) A shower powered by a bicycle

D) A window cleaning contraption powered by a bicycle

068

The first recognizable bicycle was invented in 1817 by a German Baron, Baron von Drais - he called it the hobbyhorse or dandyhorse - how did it work?

A) Instead of foot pedals there were arm pedals

B) By winding up a mechanism before setting off

C) By a complicated and inefficient chain mechanism

D) By simply pushing yourself along by your feet

069

The first bike that became popular originated in France - it was made out of wood and had a larger front wheel. What was its popular name?

A) The Penny Black
B) The Bone Shaker
C) The Tooth Grinder
D) The Bouncing Booby

070

Early bikes were quite basic, they didn't have brakes like today's bikes so what was the best method of slowing down and stopping?

A) Putting your feet down
B) Pedalling backwards
C) Jumping off
D) Using a wooden block strapped to your heel

071

Which of these was the last to be invented?

A) The bicycle
B) The steam carriage
C) The lawnmower
D) The camera

Vehicles

Tires were invented twice - the first time was in 1845 and they were fitted to horse-drawn carriages but nobody took much notice. However, the second time they were fitted to, the now popular, bicycles - they were a great success. Who was this second inventive genius?

A) Peter Tread
B) Alfred Michelin
C) Walter Raleigh
D) John Dunlop

072

What powered the first motorcycle?
A) Petrol
B) Diesel
C) Steam
D) Coal

073

What was the first vehicle to travel faster than a horse?
A) Stephenson's 'Rocket'
B) Bicycle
C) Benz car
D) Wright brother's airplane

074

075

Which of these inventors gave his name to a type of engine?

A) Peter Stroke
B) Arthur Petrol
C) William Turbo
D) Rudolf Diesel

076

Twenty years after the invention of the motor car, Mary Anderson came up with an invention that made driving much safer - what was it?

A) Windscreen wipers
B) The safety belt
C) The horn
D) Anti-locking brakes

077

Berta Benz, wife of Karl Benz, was the first person to take a long distance car journey. She borrowed her husband's newly invented tricycle-car and set off to visit relatives 75 miles away. Which of these did not happen to her on her journey?

A) Repaired a short circuit with a garter
B) Unblocked a fuel line with a hairpin
C) Patched the tires with leather strips
D) Refueled with dry cleaning fuel

Cars

The internal combustion engine has gone through many modifications. The first engine delivered one horsepower. Today Formula 1 cars have incredibly powerful engines - what is their horsepower?

A) 80 horsepower

B) 400 horsepower

C) 600 horsepower

D) 800 horsepower

When cars were first invented they had little in the way of safety features. What was the first one invented?

A) The seatbelt

B) A parachute to slow the car down when braking

C) A large net on the front fender to scoop up pedestrians

D) Windscreen wipers

The very first cars that appeared on the road were popularly known as something other than automobiles, what was it?

A) Noisy Normans

B) Smoking horses

C) Puffing autos

D) Horseless carriages

081

Who invented the steam engine?
- **A)** Archimedes, an Ancient Greek
- **B)** Hero, another Ancient Greek
- **C)** James Watt
- **D)** George Stephenson

082

Nicolas Cugnot invented the first steam powered vehicle in 1769; it didn't run on rails and it was very heavy and hard to control. What was its maximum speed?
- **A)** 2.5 mph (4 kph)
- **B)** 5 mph (8 kph)
- **C)** 10 mph (16 kph)
- **D)** 15 mph (24 kph)

083

What happened to this first steam vehicle; Cugnot, its inventor, ended up in prison)?
- **A)** It ran down a hill and killed a man
- **B)** It crashed into a wall causing lots of damage
- **C)** It blew up
- **D)** It ran into a lake

Doctors feared for people's safety when traveling by train; what did they predict would happen to them?

A) They would get thrown from the carriages and break their bones

B) They would get too hot and expire

C) That traveling at speed you wouldn't be able to breathe

D) That you would lose your sense of direction and not be able to find your way home

084

The first railway ran from Stockton to Darlington, it was 25 miles long - what year did it open?

A) 1825

B) 1837

C) 1850

D) 1875

085

Richard Trevithick invented a steam engine that traveled on rails - what did he call it?

A) The Bullet

B) The Runaway Horse

C) Catch Me Who Can

D) The Iron Dragon

086

087

George Stephenson invented and built the 'Rocket.' What was the 'Rocket?'

A) The first motorized bicycle

B) The first car to travel faster than 30mph

C) The first powered vessel to blast off from Earth

D) The first steam locomotive to carry passengers

088

George Stephenson did not go to school; which one of these was one of his jobs as a boy?

A) Selling sweets to travelers on the horse-drawn railway

B) Chimney sweep

C) Mining coal

D) Stopping cattle straying on to the horse-drawn railway line

089

The 'Stanley Steamer' was the ultimate steam-powered car. In 1906 it held the world land speed record - how fast did it go?

A) 35 mph

B) 94 mph

C) 127 mph

D) 168 mph

Steam

William Huskisson MP (a British politician) was mad about steam engines and he got to ride alongside George Stephenson in the 'Rocket' at the opening of the first ever railway - what happened to him.

- **A)** He was run over and killed by the 'Rocket'
- **B)** He inhaled too much steam and passed out
- **C)** He was travel sick
- **D)** He got overexcited and jumped out of the 'Rocket' and broke his leg

---

Stephenson's 'Rocket' had to take part in trials to see which engine would be used on the first railway. The other engines didn't do too well, which of these didn't happen to one of the other engines in the trial?

- **A)** One blew up, was repaired but sprayed everyone with boiling water
- **B)** One had the wrong shape wheels for the rails and so fell off the track
- **C)** One shot red hot coal from its chimney
- **D)** One broke down before getting to the trials

092

The Montgolfier brothers invented the first hot air balloon to carry people; but which of these creatures was on the first flight?

- **A)** A duck
- **B)** A monkey
- **C)** A goldfish
- **D)** A dog

093

Louis-Sebastian Lenormand is often credited with inventing the parachute - how far did he jump on his first daring leap?

- **A)** 130ft/40m
- **B)** 33ft/10m
- **C)** 13ft/4m
- **D)** 1,300ft/396m

094

The credit for the invention of the parachute should really go to André Garnerin in 1797 - he had great faith in his own invention, what did he do (and survive)?

- **A)** Launch himself off a very high cliff
- **B)** Launch himself from a tall tower
- **C)** Launch himself from a high mountain
- **D)** Launch himself from a hot air balloon

Flying Machines

Wilbur and Orville Wright made the first ever powered flight, they took off from Kitty Hawk, North Carolina in December 1903. The flight covered 120ft/37m at an altitude of just 10ft/3m. How long did it last?

    A) 5 minutes
    B) 2 minutes
    C) 40 seconds
    D) 12 seconds

How did the Wright brothers decide who would be the first to fly their 'Flyer?'

    A) Tossing a coin
    B) The oldest brother got to choose
    C) Cutting cards
    D) One of the brothers was too afraid of heights to fly

The Wright brothers made all kinds of breakthroughs with their flying machines; one of their most important inventions is still used by most aircraft today - what was it?

    A) Ailerons - the bits on the wings that move
    B) A moveable tail
    C) Retractable landing wheels
    D) Ejector seats

Flying Machines

098

What groundbreaking invention ended up in a cabbage patch on the farm of the inventor's Aunt Effie, after a modest 46ft/14 m flight in 1926?

A) The first helicopter
B) The first jet engine
C) The first nuclear missile
D) The first liquid fuel rocket

099

The very first rotary-wing aircraft (helicopter) to get off the ground was invented in 1907 by Paul Cornu. It had a small engine and was virtually uncontrollable - how was it stabilized?

A) By men on the ground with long sticks
B) By a large balloon of hot air
C) By turning a large screw in the opposite direction to the blades
D) By large glider wings

100

This first helicopter was destroyed on landing - how long did that first flight last?

A) 30 seconds
B) 10 seconds
C) 20 seconds
D) 1 minute

Flying Machines

How long did it take German passenger airships to cross the Atlantic?

   A) 2 days

   B) 4 days

   C) 6 days

   D) 8 days

During World War II America built the largest bomber ever, the B-29, this huge aircraft was used to drop atomic bombs on Japan. It was called 'Enola Gay' - why?

   A) They were code words for 'deadly weapon'

   B) After the pilot's mother

   C) It was the title of a popular song

   D) After the town where it was built

The Lockheed SR-71 is a high-altitude spy plane - it flies faster than any other aircraft. What is its top speed?

   A) 1211 mph/1950 kph

   B) 1526 mph/2457 kph

   C) 1973 mph/3177 kph

   D) 2193 mph /3531 kph

104 Leonardo da Vinci came up with designs for various flying machines. How did he imagine most of his flying machines would be powered?

    A) By a horse on a treadmill
    B) By a man flapping his arms
    C) By burning wood shavings
    D) By a man pedaling a type of bicycle

---

105 What was odd about Leonardo's notebooks?

    A) He wrote in code
    B) He wrote in invisible ink
    C) He wrote in mirror writing
    D) He wrote in Ancient Greek

---

106 Leonardo was not keen on war but he invented some amazing weapons - he invented a rotating crossbow machine that contained four crossbows that could be fired in rapid succession - how did it rotate?

    A) By water - it was a large water wheel
    B) By a horse on a treadmill
    C) By wind power
    D) By four men running on top of the wheel

Leonardo invented a parachute that would have worked with a few modifications - what was the main problem with Leonardo's design?

A) It needed to be made of something stronger than paper

B) It needed more ropes to stop it turning inside out

C) It needed a better launching system

D) It needed a hole in the top to stop it swinging about

Leonardo experimented with various ways of powering his flying machines many of which were quite wacky. Which of these was one of Leonardo's ideas?

A) The pilot turned a wheel that bent a bow that fired the flying machine

B) Twenty swans would be attached and their wing power would lift the machine

C) Cow saliva would fuel a helicopter

D) A horse on a treadmill drove massive wings

109 Leonardo invented all kinds of weird things - which of these wasn't one of his inventions?

- **A)** A spring-driven car
- **B)** A mechanical lion that could walk a few steps
- **C)** A robotic suit of armor that could sit down by itself
- **D)** A mechanical singing canary

110 Leonardo was fascinated by water and he invented a workable diving helmet - that would allow the diver to stay under water for some time - what else did he invent to help explore the underwater world?

- **A)** Underwater gloves
- **B)** Goggles
- **C)** Flippers
- **D)** Underwater torch

111 Which of these machines did Leonardo come up with except his was powered by four men rather than an enormous engine?

- **A)** The steam engine
- **B)** The tank
- **C)** The paddle steamer
- **D)** The submarine

Thomas Edison

The first domestic electric lights came with warnings and reassurances, which one of these was not part of Edison's accompanying notice?

- **A)** Do not attempt to light with a match
- **B)** It will not cause blindness
- **C)** It is not detrimental to health
- **D)** It does not affect the soundness of sleep

Thomas Edison was one of the most prolific of inventors; how many patents did he file?

- **A)** 1,093
- **B)** 593
- **C)** 367
- **D)** 164

Thomas Edison set up his invention factory in 1876 - he set him and his team high targets. His mission was to create a minor innovation - how often?

- **A)** Every day
- **B)** Every 10 days
- **C)** Every 10 weeks
- **D)** Every 10 months

Thomas Edison

115

In 1888 Thomas Edison invented the kinetoscope - a projector for moving films, in 1903 he made the first movie with a plot - what was it?

A) The Great and the Good
B) The Great Escape
C) The Greatest Story Ever Told
D) The Great Train Robbery

116

Thomas Edison rescued a boy from certain death on the railway. The boy's father had no money but he wanted to thank Edison so he taught him something that would change his life - what was it?

A) How to write shorthand
B) How to drive a steam train
C) Morse code and how to use the telegraph
D) How to make batteries

117

Which of these did Edison not invent?

A) Phonograph (record player)
B) Jet fuel engine
C) Electrical Vote Recorder
D) Kinetograph (motion picture camera)

The Chinese invented moveable type in the 11th century (it was not invented in Europe until 1440). However, there was one major problem for the Chinese typesetters - what was it?

A) The letters were very complicated and so difficult to print

B) There was no standardized spelling

C) Chinese has 80,000 different symbols

D) Paper had not been invented

118

The printing press was pretty much an instant success in Europe. By 1500 how many books had been printed?

A) 100,000,000

B) 10,000,000

C) 1,000,000

D) 100,000

119

The first personal computer to go on sale to the public was the Apple II. What year did it go on sale?

A) 1960

B) 1977

C) 1970

D) 1967

120

121

Blaise Pascal was a mathematical genius - in 1642, at the age of 19, he invented something to help his father who was a tax collector. What was it?

A) Double-entry bookkeeping
B) Times tables
C) Digital calculator
D) Computer

122

How many computers were there in use around the world in 1965 (bearing in mind that each computer cost nearly $750,000 in today's money)?

A) 2,000
B) 20,000
C) 200,000
D) 2,000,000

123

Which of these significant inventions dates back before the microchip and the home computer?

A) The CD
B) E-mail
C) The mouse
D) The World Wide Web

Weapons

What was invented in Europe in 1561, although it had actually been used by the Chinese over 500 years earlier?

A) Crossbow
B) Rifle
C) Cannon
D) Hand grenade

124

The Paris Gun was the gun with the longest range ever used. It was used to shell Paris in World War I; how far could it fire?

A) 36 miles (58km)
B) 16 miles (26km)
C) 76 miles (122km)
D) 56 miles (90km)

125

The Nobel Peace Prize is named after Alfred Nobel who was the inventor of something deadly. He left much of his fortune to fund the Nobel prizes. Which of the following did he invent?

A) Dynamite
B) Atomic bomb
C) Shotgun
D) Hand grenade

126

127 Who invented gunpowder in the 9th century A.D.?

A) Indian princes
B) Japanese scientists
C) Chinese alchemists
D) French soldiers

---

128 The Longbow was invented in the Welsh borders; it was much more deadly than the crossbow. A skilled bowman could rain down six arrows a minute and at what distance could he pierce the best armor of the day?

A) 150ft/50m
B) 1,650ft/500m
C) 2,500ft750m
D) 500ft/150m

---

129 In 1861 Richard Gatling invented a very deadly gun - it was the first practical machine gun. How many rounds could it fire in a minute?

A) 3,000
B) 300
C) 30
D) 13

What gruesome invention was popularly called 'Old Sparky?' More than 4,000 people were killed by it?

A) The Gatling gun
B) Dynamite
C) The electric chair
D) Smith & Weston gun

Once the Guillotine became popular, experiments started on the best kind of blade - in 1792 the oblique blade was accepted as the best and fastest blade. How quickly could it decapitate someone?

A) One second
B) 1/70 second
C) 1/30 second
D) 1/10 second

The first handguns appeared in the 14th century, they were really mini-cannons. What discovery had made them possible?

A) Cast-iron
B) Brass
C) Bullets
D) Gunpowder

130

131

132

133

What bomb, weighing more than four tons, had to be dropped from a specially adapted plane when it was traveling at 220mph/354kmph at exactly 66ft/20m above the water and released 300ft/150m from its target? This bomb had a starring role in the film 'The Dam Busters,' what was it?

A) The bouncing bomb
B) The atomic bomb
C) The doodlebug
D) The Messerschmitt

134

The early cannon was a great invention but very heavy and cumbersome - it was no good on the battlefield as it could not be moved. At the Battle of Agincourt the English bowmen devastated the French. How many English soldiers were thought to have been killed by the French cannons?

A) 0
B) 1
C) 10
D) 50

James Puckle, a London lawyer, invented the first firearm that could fire several shots without reloading. What was odd about it?

135

A) To fire it you had to sit down and strap it to your knee

B) He designed it to fire square bullets at infidels and round ones at Christians

C) You could only fire it lying on the floor

D) No one could design a satisfactory bullet to fit it

Nitroglycerine was invented by accident in 1846 by Ascanio Sobrero. Alfred Nobel went on to develop the explosive, which he called 'dynamite.' What happened to Nobel early on in its development?

136

A) The factory exploded, killing his brother

B) He blew off his right arm

C) The factory exploded, killing his entire family

D) He blew off his left leg

137 **W**ho invented the first flush toilet?

    A) Thomas Crapper
    B) Sir John Harrington
    C) Josiah Wedgwood
    D) Archimedes

138 **I**n the history of the toilet there is some debate as to what, a London plumber, Thomas Crapper's contribution was. What did he actually invent?

    A) The overhead cistern
    B) The valveless water cistern
    C) Toilet paper
    D) The wooden toilet seat

139 **A**lexander Cummings made a significant modification to the toilet in 1775 - what was it?

    A) The toilet seat
    B) The self-filling flush
    C) The S-bend - to stop nasty smells
    D) A working connection to mains drains

Hubert Cecil Booth at the beginning of 20th century produced a cumbersome horse-drawn device that was used to suck dust from houses: a kind of forerunner to the vacuum cleaner. What was its nickname?

A) Groaning Gordon
B) Bellowing Bertha
C) Whining Winnie
D) Puffing Billy

Who marketed his invention in 1926 with the slogan 'It beats as it sweeps as it cleans?'

A) Charles Sweeper
B) Thomas Ewbank
C) William Hoover
D) Melville Bissell

What was the main aim of the inventors of the earliest dishwashers?

A) To save time
B) To save water
C) To prevent breakages
D) To preserve the washer-upper's hands

143 John Curtis invented chewing gum in 1848 - what was its main ingredient?

A) Sap of a spruce tree
B) India rubber
C) Sap of the maple tree
D) Corn starch

144 Dr. John Stith Pemberton invented a drink which had to be renamed - it became Coca-Cola but its original name was dropped in 1885 when alcohol was banned in Atlanta, Georgia. What was its original name?

A) Whisky and coke
B) Gin cola
C) Jamaican rum and cola
D) French wine of Coca

145 Bubblegum was invented by Frank Henry Fleer in 1906 - it wasn't very successful because it was too sticky. What was it called?

A) Sticky-Ticky
B) Fleer-Flubber
C) Bibble-Bubble
D) Blibber-Blubber

Food

Who invented the Corn Flake in 1906?

146

  A) Arthur Nestlé
  B) Will Keith Kellogg
  C) Peter Nabisco
  D) Frances Breakfast

Who first discovered that food frozen quickly under pressure froze without the formation of ice crystals and so preserved the texture of the food?

147

  A) Ralph Findus
  B) Clarence Birdseye
  C) Stefan Walls
  D) Rupert Popsicle

A chef called George Crum worked at a restaurant in New York and he invented a whole new way of eating potatoes. What did he create in 1853 to annoy an extremely fussy customer?

148

  A) French fries
  B) Mashed potato
  C) Potato chips (crisps)
  D) Potato waffles

149

An 11-year-old boy called Frank Epperson had a happy accident in 1905 - the result of which was an invention that has been popular every since. What did he invent?

A) Milk shake
B) The popsicle (ice-lolly)
C) Pretzels
D) Popcorn

150

The Ancient Egyptians enjoyed their sweet treats - which of these did they invent?

A) Sugar almonds
B) Toffee
C) Fudge
D) Marshmallows

151

The sandwich was famously invented by John Montague - Earl of Sandwich - what was he doing that he needed a portable snack?

A) Hunting stags
B) Sailing
C) Gambling
D) Juggling

Food

The first breakfast cereal was invented in 1892 by Henry Perkey - which one was it?

A) Branflakes
B) Weetabix
C) Shredded Wheat
D) Rice Krispies

In 1904 Thomas Sullivan invented the tea bag - what were his first bags made of?

A) Extra strong tissue paper
B) Linen
C) Nylon stockings
D) Silk

Melitta Bentz invented something in 1908 which enhanced everybody's coffee drinking experience - what was it?

A) The coffee filter
B) The cafetière
C) The coffee grinder
D) Instant coffee

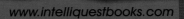

155

The first person we know of who experimented with freezing food was Francis Bacon, an English lawyer. Sadly, in 1626 he came to an unfortunate end, what happened to him?

A) He caught a chill after stuffing a chicken with snow on a cold night

B) He froze to death in his own ice house

C) He was found frozen to death by the side of his lake clutching a frozen trout

D) He froze his hands so badly that he got frostbite and died of complications

156

In 1867 Napoleon III launched a competition to find a substitute for butter that was both cheaper and longer lasting. The result was margarine - which of these ingredients was not in the first margarine?

A) Warmed milk

B) Minced pig's stomach

C) Eggs

D) Suet

Marion Donovan was an American mother and inventor - she invented the first leak-proof disposable diaper (nappy). What did she line the first ones with?

157

A) Plastic bags
B) Cellophane
C) Shower curtains
D) Bicycle inner tubes

What invention (or more accurately re-invention) was banned by the Church in the 11th century for being blasphemous?

158

A) The fork
B) The scissors
C) The compass
D) Nail clippers

Samuel Johnson was approached to write the first comprehensive English dictionary and it was published in 1775 but how long did it take for him to compile it?

159

A) 55 years
B) 23 years
C) 10 months
D) 11 years

160 The first lock to use a small flat key was invented in 1848. What was the name of the inventor?

    A) Andrew Mortis
    B) Linus Yale
    C) Christopher Chubb
    D) Roger Banham

161 Benjamin Franklin was particularly interested in electricity but he invented other things. Which of these was his invention?

    A) False teeth
    B) The pocket watch
    C) Wellington boots
    D) Bifocal spectacles

162 Fire was a prehistoric invention but up until the 1820s it was still hard to create fire instantly. What invention changed all that?

    A) The tinder box
    B) The lighter
    C) The safety match
    D) The gas lamp

The 'Penny Black' was a small but significant invention; what was it?

A) A minted coin
B) A light bulb
C) A bicycle tire
D) A postage stamp

The first jukebox appeared in 1890 - in its first six months it took more than $1,000; why was this remarkable?

A) It could not play music at a constant speed
B) It only played one song
C) The music jumped all the time
D) You had to wind it up between each song to make it play

What does the X in X-ray stand for?

A) X – short for explosion
B) X – a symbol scientists use for things they don't understand
C) X – short for excellent
D) X – marks the spot

166 Sir James Dewar was an important Scottish scientist, however his serious scientific research led him to a useful everyday invention - which one?

A) The thermos flask
B) The microwave
C) The vacuum cleaner
D) The thermometer

167 The perpetual mousetrap was invented in 1860 - how could it go on catching so many mice?

A) It catapulted the dead mice out of the trap
B) It had a trap door
C) It was a pad that electrocuted the mice rather than trapped them
D) It was a whole circle of separate traps

168 What popular invention started life as a tin and cocktail shaker?

A) Coffee percolator
B) Hi-fi speakers
C) Lava lamp
D) Kettle

Miscellaneous everyday

Earle Dickson had an accident-prone wife - he would come home from work every night and find her cut or burned from her efforts in the kitchen. What did he invent in 1920 to ease her suffering?

A) Adhesive bandages
B) Oven gloves
C) Antiseptic cream
D) Aspirin

The hearing aid went through many developments in the beginning of the 20th century. However, up until 1935 a hearing aid weighed 15.5lb/7kg - what was weighing it down?

A) A large trumpet to amplify sound
B) A large carbon microphone
C) A large valve amplifier
D) Huge batteries

What did Carlton Magee invent in 1932 that has not made him universally popular?

A) The parking meter
B) The wheel clamp
C) The speed camera
D) Sleeping policemen - traffic humps

172

In 1936 Percy Shaw invented small reflecting glass lenses to be placed in the road to guide motorists in the dark; which animal was his inspiration?

A) Sheep
B) Dog
C) Cat
D) Bat

173

Quartz watches are now incredibly cheap but the first ones that went on sale at Christmas 1969 were expensive - what else could you have bought for the price of a Quartz watch?

A) A television
B) A transistor radio
C) A small house
D) A medium-sized car

174

Frances Gabe hated housework - so much so that she came up with a radical invention - what was it?

A) Disposable crockery and clothes
B) Self-cleaning clothes
C) A fully self-cleaning house
D) A dust and dirt-free house

What started life as a tin of cat food inside a coffee tin connected to a vacuum cleaner?

A) The vacuum flask
B) The pressure cooker
C) Air-conditioning unit
D) The hovercraft

175

What very handy gadget was first issued to new army recruits in one European army in 1891?

A) Can opener
B) Swiss army knife
C) Italian espresso maker
D) German perpetual motion watch

176

A metal can for preserving food was invented in 1810. However the can opener was not invented for another 50 years. How did you open the first cans?

A) By hitting it with a hammer and chisel
B) With a very sharp knife
C) By heating it up - the lid would blow off
D) With a small explosive charge attached to the lid

177

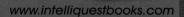

178

What did Gail Borden invent that proved of great use to soldiers in the American Civil War?

- **A)** Corned beef
- **B)** Evaporated milk
- **C)** Rapid firing rifle
- **D)** Waterproof boots

179

In 1802 Frederic Albert Winsor in 1802 hosted a dinner party, what was remarkable about it?

- **A)** The food had all been previously frozen
- **B)** The food was cooked by Bunsen burners at the table
- **C)** The food was cooked by gas
- **D)** The food was cooked on a barbecue

180

A French hairdresser Alexandre Godefroy invented a hairdryer in the 1880s - how was it powered?

- **A)** A tube connected to a gas stove
- **B)** A compact steam engine
- **C)** An enormous DC battery
- **D)** A small diesel engine

Eadweard Muybridge invented a process that created moving pictures - he used 12 cameras in a line. What was he trying to prove with his first set of moving pictures?

181

A) That a cancan dancer's legs go higher than their heads

B) That a rabbit jumps using all four feet

C) That a galloping horse sometimes has all four feet off the ground

D) That a bird's wings are sometimes still

Eadweard Muybridge's behavior was quite weird - what was thought to be the cause of his oddness?

182

A) He never went to bed

B) He never ate - only drank

C) He had all kinds of nervous tics which meant he couldn't talk properly

D) He had suffered serious brain damage in a bus accident

Photography

183

W illiam Fox Talbot came up with many of the key inventions that made photography possible - what was his initial inspiration?

- **A)** Wanting a record of his children's development
- **B)** His bad memory
- **C)** Wanting to capture an enduring image of his new wife
- **D)** His inability to draw

184

G eorge Eastman was responsible for making photography within everybody's reach - he called his new camera Kodak - what does it mean?

- **A)** Greek for 'picture'
- **B)** Czech for 'remember'
- **C)** It's a made-up, meaningless word
- **D)** German for 'look'

185

I n 1947 Edwin Land made his fortune by inventing a new kind of camera - what was it?

- **A)** The Polaroid camera
- **B)** The camcorder
- **C)** The disposable camera
- **D)** The digital camera

Photography

In 1900 George Eastman invented the first truly affordable camera - it was sold for 5 shillings (25p/40 cents) - what was it called?

A) The Instamatic
B) The Box Brownie
C) The One Click
D) The Handy Andy

The Lumière brothers produced the first ever moving films, they showed them to an amazed audience in 1895, the films lasted one minute, what was the subject of the first film they made?

A) Workers leaving a factory
B) Eating breakfast
C) Magic tricks
D) A walk in the park

The oldest surviving photograph in the world was taken in the 1820s - how long was its exposure time (today the exposure time is a fraction of a second)?

A) 8 seconds
B) 8 minutes
C) 8 hours
D) 8 days

Games and Toys

189

What was the original Frisbee?

A) A vinyl record
B) A plastic plate
C) A dustbin lid
D) A pie tin

190

The first real chess computer was invented in 1958, and then went through many modifications - the computer became known as Deep Blue. What year did it finally beat Gary Kasparov the world's best chess player?

A) 1967
B) 1977
C) 1987
D) 1997

191

What was invented in 1750 as a teaching aid in Geography lessons?

A) Jigsaw puzzles
B) Flat maps
C) Compass
D) Globes

What game was invented in 1823 in an English school?

A) Rugby
B) Tennis
C) Squash
D) Hockey

Alfred Butts invented Scrabble in the 1930s, he worked out the value of the letters by counting how frequently they appeared on a page of text, what page did he use?

A) First page of the Bible
B) First page of Tom Sawyer by Mark Twain
C) Long letter from his boss giving him the sack
D) Front page of the New York Times

The first Teddy bears appeared in the US in 1902, they were named after a US president, which one?

A) Theodore Roosevelt
B) Benjamin Franklin
C) Abraham Lincoln
D) George Washington

195

'The Turk' was thought to be a revolutionary invention (in fact it was a great illusion); it toured Europe and amazed Napoleon - what was it?

A) A robot that actually concealed a small boy

B) A magic music box that actually concealed a harpsichord

C) A chess computer that concealed a real chess player

D) A computer that could answer general knowledge questions

196

In what year did the 'Game Boy' appear?

A) 1989

B) 1985

C) 1999

D) 1995

197

Which popular toy was invented in ancient China to frighten evil spirits?

A) Yo-yo

B) Kite

C) Hula-hoop

D) Pogo stick

What toy was invented in 1943 by a naval engineer, and is still made on the original machines?

A) Hula Hoops
B) Lego
C) Play-doh
D) Slinky

Which of these sweets came first?

A) Pez
B) Cotton Candy/Candyfloss
C) Life Savers
D) M & Ms

What was invented in 1956 as a wallpaper cleaner and made its inventor a millionaire while still in his twenties?

A) Fuzzy Felt
B) Glitter glue
C) Play-doh
D) Magic sand

Which of these is not an ancient game?
- **A)** Marbles
- **B)** Hopscotch
- **C)** Bowling
- **D)** Tennis

Which game was created in 14 days by a teacher who needed an energetic game for one of his rowdy classes?
- **A)** Baseball
- **B)** Soccer
- **C)** Tennis
- **D)** Basketball

What were golf balls originally filled with?
- **A)** Feathers
- **B)** Pebbles
- **C)** Sand
- **D)** Pig fat

The first aerosol spray can was invented in 1944 by two scientists working for the US Dept of Agriculture. What were they trying to control?

204

A) Locusts that were attacking crops in Texas

B) Swarms of killer bees

C) Tics on beef cattle

D) Malaria-carrying mosquitoes

There is one invention for which there have been more patents than you would imagine - barbed wire. How many designs of barbed wire were there at the heyday of its importance?

205

A) More than 1,200

B) More than 240

C) More than 120

D) More than 400

The first combine harvester was patented in 1836; how many horses did it take to pull the largest of these early combines?

206

A) 15

B) 40

C) 50

D) 80

207

George Washington Carver (1864-1943) was an agricultural chemist, he was an African American born of slave parents. He was an ingenious man, which of these is one of his claims to fame?

A) He invented the tractor

B) He came up with 325 different uses for surplus peanuts

C) He invented powerful insecticides

D) He invented 82 uses for cotton waste

208

The wheelbarrow seems to have been invented by the Chinese more than 2,000 years ago - it was used by their armies for moving heavy loads. In 1975 James Dyson invented a modification to this ancient invention - what was it?

A) He replaced the wheel with a ball that didn't sink into soft ground

B) He developed a large super-thin wheel to make the wheelbarrow travel faster

C) He added two wheels to the back to make it easier to push

D) He added a motor to the front wheel to power the barrow

Chindogu

In Japan they love useless inventions
and they even have a special word for
it — "Chindogu." Chindogu inventions must
not be patented or sold but they must be
manufactured. Here are a few of their
crazy ideas.

I n Japan they work long hours and often
have long commutes and so there are
many chindogu to help the commuter catch
up on their sleep - which of these hasn't been
invented?

A) Commuter's helmet with a suction
pad to keep head upright when asleep
and a message on the front saying at
which station the commuter needs
to get off

B) Small tape recorder activated every
time the doors open which asks
fellow commuters to wake up the
sleeper at required station

C) Neck brace that rests on the floor
and enables the commuter to sleep
standing up

D) Subway sleeper's screen - it covers
the face, muffles any snoring sounds
and tells other commuters where
the sleeper needs to get off

209

210 What did one inventor attach to his cat to help keep the house as he liked it?

A) A brush to its tail

B) Special Velcro-like pads to its tail to pick up any cat hair left behind

C) A little tin of air-freshener that squirted every time the cat jumped

D) Dusters to its feet

---

211 Which of these was designed to make getting about the busy streets of Tokyo safer?

A) A flashing orange light attached to your head to alert cars when you were crossing the road.

B) A hat with a tape recorder that broadcast a message asking people to get out of your way

C) A portable zebra crossing that you can unroll when you need to cross the road

D) A specially padded body suit to soften the impact of slow moving vehicles that bump into you as you cross the road

Chindogu

What chindogu was designed to make going to night clubs more enjoyable?

A) A combined megaphone and ear-trumpet (shaped like a coke bottle) to make talking and listening easier

B) Earplug earrings to deaden the noise

C) A thin lining for clothes full of iced water to keep you cool

D) Disco shoe insoles that were full of cooling gel that gently massaged your feet, the more you dance the more they massage your feet

---

One inventor proposed a food cooler for bowls of steaming noodles - how did it work?

A) It was a box spraying a mist of very cold dry ice

B) It was a specially created bowl that was very heat absorbent

C) It was a mini-fan that you attached to the underside of your arm

D) It was a special attachment that you fixed to your lips containing iced water

Chindogu

214

What hat?

What was special about the chindogu hay fever hat?

- **A)** It had a fine gauze netting to catch airborne irritants
- **B)** It had a roll of toilet tissue conveniently attached to the hat
- **C)** It had special goggle-like glasses attached that contained eye drops to soothe the eyes
- **D)** It had special nose filters attached to it

215

The personal rainsaver is an ecologically sound invention (if not hugely practical); what was its design?

- **A)** A large hat with bowl attached, connected to a pipe that feeds into your briefcase
- **B)** An inside-out umbrella that feeds a tank carried like a shoulder bag
- **C)** A coat made out of a very absorbent fabric that soaks up the rain and feeds it into special pockets
- **D)** A large funnel that you attach to your car - the water is collected in a bowl on the back seat

More Mad Inventions

These are all mad inventions that have actually been patented.

What was a 'charvolant?' (It was invented in 1828 by George Pocock).

A) A tricycle with a lawn-cutting attachment behind

B) A bicycle adapted for use in the water

C) A tricycle powered by two kites

D) A bicycle that could pull a large padded chair

By 1880 a very effective food mincer for the kitchen had been patented - there was a smaller version for use on the table - who or what was it designed for?

A) Babies and small children

B) Those who had lost their teeth

C) Taking the lumps out of mashed potato

D) Thinning soup for those who did not like lumps

More Mad Inventions

218

What was special about the rocking horse invented by John Hircock (it never really caught on)?

A) It had a special mechanism that imitated the horse jumping

B) You could lengthen and shorten its legs

C) You could ride it on the open road at a gallop

D) It neighed as it rocked

219

All of these inventions sound completely mad but one does actually have some value (although it never caught on), which one?

A) Ear muffs for chickens - to stop them being disturbed by other chickens

B) Clogs for chickens - to stop their feet rotting

C) Jackets for chickens - to stop them pulling out their feathers

D) Glasses for chickens - to stop them pecking each other's eyes out

More Mad Inventions

Patented in 1902, what special feature did the 'improved cup and saucer,' boast?

A) A large lip to catch drips

B) A weight at the base of the cup to keep it stable

C) Drainage channels in the saucer, to keep the cup dry

D) A warming pad in the saucer to keep the tea warm

220

What was the purpose of an evil-looking bit of machinery that was patented in 1896 - all to look more beautiful?

A) A dimple producer

B) A permanent beauty spot creator

C) A permanent eyelash curler

D) A lip pout enhancer

221

The Natural Flying Machine was proposed in 1865, although it was probably never built and certainly it never flew - how was it powered?

A) By a horse on a treadmill

B) By three strong men with large oar-like wings

C) By 10 eagles in harnesses

D) Three enormous kites

222

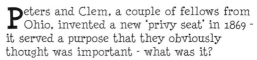

223

Peters and Clem, a couple of fellows from Ohio, invented a new 'privy seat' in 1869 - it served a purpose that they obviously thought was important - what was it?

A) It massaged your bottom to help you relax

B) It had special rollers to stop people standing on the seat

C) It had a timing buzzer that went off if you had been sitting there too long

D) It had a special smell sensor that dispensed air freshener depending on how great the need

224

In 1979 James McGalliard invented a truly different pair of pantyhose - they weren't just pantyhose; what else did they do?

A) They contained depilatory cream to remove unwanted hair

B) They contained a detergent that made them self-cleaning

C) They warned you when you had been standing for too long and needed to sit down

D) They massaged your thighs and bottom to help eliminate cellulite

Pasquale Nigro was concerned for the safety of people in tall buildings - he decided that there needed to be improvements in fire escapes - what did he patent as the answer?

A) Your own personal escape ladder that you could take with you - it had extremely powerful sucker pads

B) A spring-loaded seat at the fire escape to be used in combination with a mini-parachute

C) A large pair of wings that could be strapped on and you could jump from any high window

D) An inflatable suit - you could jump and you would bounce

A man-catching tank was invented in 1921 - it had many splendid features designed for catching burglars - how did it catch its man?

A) With a giant net

B) With a pair of giant claws

C) With an electric stun gun

D) It didn't, it shot him!

225

226

227

A special number plate that you could reverse to change its color was patented in the UK. What was the purpose of changing the color of the number plate?

  A) To warn other drivers as to what mood the driver was is in

  B) To warn other drivers that the driver was over 65

  C) To warn other drivers there was a baby in the car

  D) To show the sex of the driver

228

Ignatius Nathaniel Soares came up with a wacky invention that, though unsightly in the short term, would result in a much more pleasing face - what was it?

  A) A nose shaper - a sort of nose patch to reshape broken and misshapen noses

  B) Eye enlargers - clips to attach to the eyes to stretch them to give you beautiful big eyes

  C) A chin reducer - a strap which when worn continually would reduce the prominence of the chin

  D) Ear clips - to pin back sticky-out ears

More Mad Inventions

Brice Belisle was very attached to his pet and did not want to leave it at home. What did he invent so he could have his pet with him at all times?

A) A T-shirt with a waterproof pouch that could be filled with water and carry a goldfish

B) A vest with tubes and chambers for his hamster

C) An elaborate hat that served as bird cage for his budgie

D) A cat carriage that allowed him to tow his cat everywhere

There is a particular machine for which the US and UK patent office receive lots of requests for patents, however it is believed that such a machine can never be built - what is the machine?

A) A time-traveling machine

B) A perpetual motion machine

C) An alchemist machine that turns metal to gold

D) A machine that turns water into wine

231 **B**adly behaved dogs can cause all kinds of problems - what device was patented in 1912 to deal with one doggy problem?

A) A nose ring with hooks attached, to stop dogs worrying sheep - the hooks got caught up in the sheep's wool and when the sheep moved the dogs nose was pulled

B) An attachment for the back-end of a dog to stop dogs smelling each other's bottoms

C) A specially adapted bicycle tire that was resistant to dog bites

D) A harmless but revolting spray, particularly for postmen, to spray at annoying dogs

232 **I**n 1916 a couple of guys from Oregon patented a new kind of scarecrow - what was different about it?

A) It had clockwork moving arms

B) It was a cat jumping

C) It made a loud rasping noise when the wind blew

D) It could walk around on mechanical legs

More Mad Inventions

Edward Doughney had a soft spot for helpless creatures, which of these did he invent and patent to help them?

A) A mini-cat flap to allow mice to escape from cats

B) A mini-ladder to attach to a bath to allow spiders to escape

C) A sensor attached to a vacuum cleaner to stop you sucking up any living creatures

D) A special bridge that could be strung across roads for squirrels to cross the road safely

233

In 1970 a Mr Young patented something that he felt would catch on amongst regular air travelers - what was it?

A) A personal safety suit, it was heat resistant and contained both a parachute and a life jacket

B) A design of a shoe that expanded as your feet did

C) A pillow that opened up and doubled as a crash helmet

D) A device that told you how fast and at what height you were traveling

234

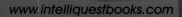

235

Captain John Benjamin Stoner invented a 'New or Improved Suit or Dress and Fittings for Saving Life in Water'. It was an India rubber and cork suit - you were kept upright in the water by lead weights in your ankles. It came with a box containing all kinds of essentials - which of these was not included?

A) Cigars
B) Reading matter
C) Pipe and tobacco
D) Shampoo

236

An Italian man called Pedruzzolli who lived in London was a keen swimmer and he invented a device that he hoped would make him a faster, more effective swimmer. What was his invention?

A) An early form of flippers with separate toes
B) Wing-like attachments for the arms, a bit like fins
C) Swimming umbrellas that opened and closed to pull you through the water
D) A propeller that you turned with your hands

A baseball hat with two large plastic ears affixed was invented to help the hard of hearing. What name was it given?

A) Nelly's Hearing Aid

B) Remember to hear all

C) The Dumb Bo Hearing Hat

D) Babar's acoustic aid

237

T his is a particularly revolting invention - and one that would make you pretty sick - it involved you swallowing something and then having to bring it back up again - what was it?

A) A tapeworm trap - a baited trap on a piece of string, you swallow it, then pulled it back up

B) A leech in a tube - you swallow it and leave it in your stomach for a few hours to help clean you out, then pull it back out

C) An acid collector - you swallow a swab of super-absorbent cotton wool treated with a secret ingredient and it soaks up excess acid

D) A swab to clear your lungs - you swallow a specially treated swab and keep it down there till it absorbed excess fluid

238

More Mad Inventions

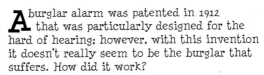

239

A burglar alarm was patented in 1912 that was particularly designed for the hard of hearing; however, with this invention it doesn't really seem to be the burglar that suffers. How did it work?

- **A)** It activated a strong flashing light
- **B)** It tipped the sleeping house owner out of bed to warn them a burglar was downstairs
- **C)** It fired a bullet into your bedroom ceiling
- **D)** It sprayed the sleeping house owner with water to warn them a burglar had just broken in

240

James Boyle patented a hat in 1896, which seemed pretty useful to him - it never caught on and has probably missed its moment. What did it do?

- **A)** Self-clean
- **B)** It could be used to send radio messages
- **C)** Create low-level electricity through a small windmill attached
- **D)** Salute to passers by

Pot Luck

Who invented the World Wide Web?
- **A)** Bill Gates
- **B)** Tim Berners-Lee
- **C)** Steve Jobs
- **D)** Richard Branson

241

Who invented the motorcycle?
- **A)** Karl Benz
- **B)** Gottlieb Daimler
- **C)** Henry Ford
- **D)** Joseph Harley

242

The first commercial robots appeared in 1956 and now nearly 50 years on there are still some things that robot designers find hard to achieve in trying to make humanoid robots. Which of these still proves a challenge?

- **A)** Being able to speak
- **B)** Having effective working hands
- **C)** Being able to walk at a reasonable speed on two legs
- **D)** Being able to lift heavy objects

243

Other Titles

There are many other exciting quiz
and puzzle books in the IntelliQuest range,
and your QUIZMO electronic unit
knows the answers to them all!

You can order from your
local bookshop or online bookseller.

For a full listing of current titles
(and ISBN numbers) see:

www.intelliquestbooks.com

LAGOON
BOOKS